A CONVERSATION
With Myself
Book 1

A guided journal with 365 days of questions that will inspire mindful conversation with yourself.

Written by Kim Dawson

A CONVERSATION
With Myself

Copyright by Kim Dawson

Publisher Tandem Services Press

PO Box 220, Yucaipa, CA 92399

www.tandomservicesink.com

Book Design by Paige Anocibar

ISBN 978-1-954986-09-1

A CONVERSATION
With Myself
Book 1

A guided journal with 365 days of questions that will inspire mindful conversation with yourself.

Written by Kim Dawson

Us, two months after Joe passed

To my kids, Blake and Ashley—
Through you, I found the courage to heal and learn to be a kid again. I am forever grateful for your love and quick wit throughout the years. We are quite the team and
I am VERY proud of us!

Us, 18 years later and living our best lives...

Introduction
Why I wrote this book

For many years now, I wanted to share my story in the hopes that I could connect with others and help them through any life struggles they might be having. I also visualized this process as an interactive book instead of just a lot of words on a page. Within this self-discovery journal, I will share my story and also ask you a lot of questions to stimulate a "conversation with yourself." There will be one question a day for a 12 month period. You will need to answer each question as detailed and as honestly as you can. Note your first thoughts, any and all feelings, and any resistance or acceptance that you experience. Observe yourself without judgment. You will revisit these same questions and answers in "Conversation with Myself, Book 2" and in "Conversation with Myself, Book 3". You will be asked to reflect on your answers and how you feel in the moment to see if you can discover any changes in your heart and/or mindset. My hope is that through this process a deeper understanding of your individual needs, strengths, and desires will be identified and either celebrated and/or finally healed.

"Something's There" Poem

I wrote this poem, "Something's There," when my husband had cancer. I thought I wrote it for him, but it became clear that it was meant for me. After he passed, I had many ups and downs on my journey to healing. There were many moments of vulnerability and empowerment and many times I felt like quitting. I wanted to share my story so you could see that you aren't alone in your journey. I want you to feel your pain and struggles knowing that I have also been right there dealing with similar emotions. This way when those issues of fear kick in, you will be able to see the "light at the end of the tunnel" like I did. It will give you the drive to keep exploring and discovering new aspects of yourself. Then you will be able to welcome yourself back into your life knowing that you are "home." YOU'VE GOT THIS!

Something's There

You're cold
You shiver and wrap your arms around yourself
You look around, but there are only heavy clouds of fog
You can't see and you're afraid to move because you might not make it
    back
You stretch your arms out, hoping to find something solid
You move your feet around on the floor to make sure there is
    something there to support you

But...you don't move

Shhh....

Something's there!

You strain your eyes to see, but it's so unclear
An image comes into view
It's close, but when you reach out, you can't touch it
It's telling you something, but...is it really?
You're confused
You cry
You're comforted by this image, but you don't know who it is
"It's here to help me. It wants to love me," you say
You feel warmer and unfold your arms from your body

But...you don't move

The image starts to leave and you scream,
"Don't leave me! I'm so lost!"

The image knows this and whispers, "Trust me!" then reaches out to
    you
You move and grab hold, afraid to let go
You look down and realize...

You're holding your own hand

Book 1 Directions

Book 1

Directions: Because the questions are labeled "Day 1", "Day 2", and so forth, it doesn't matter when you start this journey of healing. Your "Day 1" starts the moment you become aware that you are in need of a change. Answer one question a day and write your answers in the space provided. There will be directions as you progress that will help guide you. Just be an observer and write down all thoughts that come to mind. Don't over analyze or judge what comes to you. Later in Book 2 and Book 3, you will be able to revisit these questions and your answers again. It will give you an opportunity to note any changes and/or commonalities present within yourself.

My Story 1

My Story 1

"Is it okay to touch her? I need to touch her. She has to know I haven't left her. Mommy is here, Sweetheart. Stay with me. DON'T LEAVE ME!"

Too scared to cry, too scared to think the worst for fear I would make it happen…. It was in this moment that I surrendered to the knowing that I was part of something bigger then me and that I needed to trust the love and support I felt from it. Within a "split second", I was recovering from a massively evasive surgery to have my 32 week old baby girl who was fighting desperately for her life, a 1 1/2 year old son at home wondering where Mommy was, and a relationship with my husband that was fragile at best. How did I get here? How do I survive this? How do I understand the purpose of this?

Day 1 - Day 3

Day 1
What do I need in my life right now?

Day 2
What is my purpose here?

Day 3
Write something positive...

Day 4 - Day 6

Day 4
What inspires me and why?

Day 5
What do I care about most?

Day 6
I feel insecure when...

Day 7
How am I proactive?

Day 8
What do I really love to do?

Day 9
What weighs me down?

Day 10

How do I get in my own way?

Day 11

What do I do to relieve stress in my life?

Day 12

How do I support others?

Day 13
The best advice I ever received and applied...

Day 14
What could make me healthier?

Day 15
What am I most proud of?

Day 16
What is my strongest quality?

Day 17
What do I fear?

Day 18
List three things I would change about myself.

Day 19
What can I do right now to make a difference?

Day 20
What do I want to be remembered for and why?

Day 21
How do I take care of myself?

Day 22

What does my life look, feel, and sound like to me?

Day 23

What did I enjoy doing as a child, and do I still do it today?
Why or why not?

Day 24

What has held me back in life?

Day 25
What can others do to help support me?

Day 26
What are my strongest beliefs?

Day 27
How do I allow myself to be vulnerable?

Day 28 - Day 30

Day 28
If I could talk to my inner child, what would he or she say to me?

Day 29
Where am I stuck?

Day 30
What does a survivor look like to me?

My Story 2

My Story 2

"I am not enough. If I had only done things differently, he might not have left. What am I lacking? I am sick to my stomach."

Two and a half months after my daughter comes home, my husband and I split up. We were in a rut and we couldn't seem to find a way to communicate and breech the canyon that separated us. I suffered a lot of self blame, self loathing, and bullied myself for not being "better." I had lost myself in my grief and fear. I just couldn't get my feet back under me. I couldn't quite exhale. There was a desperation in me that I had never experienced before. I despised myself for feeling this weak and vulnerable.

Day 31
I smile when...

Day 32
How do I express myself to the world?
(Do I sing, write, etc.)

Day 33
What do my clothes say about me?

Day 34
How can I better take care of myself?

Day 35
My natural talents and gifts are?

Day 36
What color am I and why?

Day 37

How would I describe myself in five words?

Day 38

I find deep satisfaction in...

Day 39

My soul sings when...

Day 40
How do I deal with other people's problems?

Day 41
How do I self-bully myself?

Day 42
I am out of balance when...

Day 43
What does forgiveness look like to me?

Day 44
What does "Be your own kind of amazing" mean? How does this connect to me?

Day 45
What do I like/value most about myself?

Day 46 - Day 48

Day 46
How do I show myself respect?

Day 47
When I am still and "listening," what do I hear?

Day 48
How do I connect with others?

Day 49
What deeply ingrained habits do I have?

Day 50
My self worth is...

Day 51
How do I want someone to love me?

Day 52
How do I begin to love myself?

Day 53
I am honoring myself when...

Day 54
How do I talk to myself?

Day 55 - Day 57

Day 55

Write a negative comment about yourself and then rewrite in a positive and self-affirming way.

Day 56

How do I want to contribute to the world?

Day 57

What do others see when they look at me?

Day 58
What do I stand for?

Day 59
What aspects of my personality hold me back?

Day 60
What do I see when I look in the mirror?

Day 61

Day 61
How can I fully align with my authentic self?

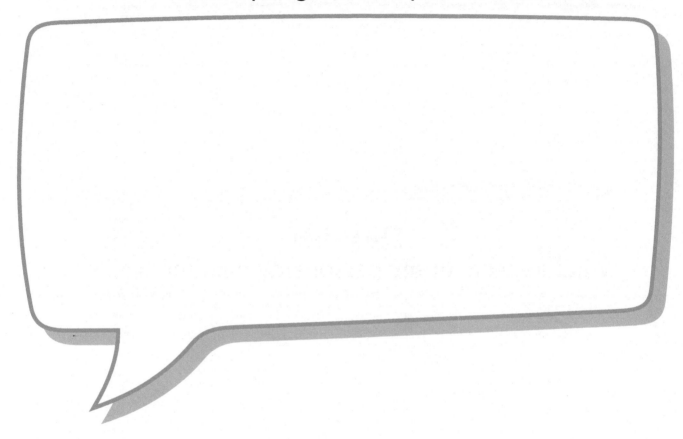

My Story 3

My Story 3

"How am I going to do this? How am I going to raise two babies by myself?"

I was lost and scared. The only comfort I could find was that "happy place" that I could glimpse occasionally. I knew my salvation was within, but I couldn't quite keep my focus on it long enough to feel the ease of my fear. I kept trying to reach for it amongst the consuming darkness. This darkness that ALWAYS seemed to threaten to take my last breath. One day at a time...one breath at a time... you can do this...focus on the kids when you feel lost...they will guide you back into the light...

Day 62
What brings me happiness?

Day 63
Who do I respect and why?

Day 64
I laugh out loud when...

Day 65
I am in balance when...

Day 66
I am at my worst...

Day 67
What are my hobbies?

Day 68 - Day 70

Day 68
How can I be more supportive of others?

Day 69
What drains my energy the most?

Day 70
What gives my life value?

Day 71

How do I show love to myself?

Day 72

What joy do I give the world?

Day 73

When am I most productive in my day?

Day 74
What does "happy" look like to me?

Day 75
What bad habits do I want to break?

Day 76
I feel confident when…

Day 77

What changes can I make that would improve my life?

Day 78

I am at my best when...

Day 79

How do I respond to criticism?

Day 80
What causes me sadness?

Day 81
How do I rewrite the bad scripts I have developed for myself?

Day 82
What would someone experience if they walked in my shoes?

Day 83
When I am following my heart...

Day 84
Describe my relationship with myself.

Day 85
How do I live in alignment with my values?

Day 86 - Day 88

Day 86
What does balance look like to me?

Day 87
How do I communicate love to others? (What is my love language?)

Day 88
If I could talk to myself as a child, what would that conversation be?

Day 89 - Day 91

Day 89
What is the story I tell myself all the time?

Day 90
What drives me?

Day 91
My life's journey is…

My Story 4

My Story 4

"You have what? You have cancer and have three to six months to live? How is that possible?"

This conversation between my husband and I happened a few months after our daughter was born. He had been to the doctor while she was in the hospital fighting for her life and was told he had stage 4 Non-Hodgkins Lymphoma. He couldn't tell me right away because he was overwhelmed himself. However, he was also worried that I wouldn't be able to take any more. Sadly, I knew he was right. We were still healing from our break up, still in love with each other, still at a loss of how to work through everything. He had moved in with another woman who previously had cancer and understood his fears. She was good to him and our kids. I was working through raising my babies despite all this pain and uncertainty. How do I take care of myself here? How do I deal with this debilitating loss and fear of the future?

Day 92
How do I feel today?

Day 93
What activities give me the most pleasure?

Day 94
What emotion am I and why?

Day 95
What are my pet peeves?

Day 96
What does success look like to me?

Day 97
What habits do I have that cause trouble for me?

Day 98
How do I "feel" today?

Day 99
My best memory is...

Day 100
What animal am I and why?

Day 101
How do I express my anger?

Day 102
How do I limit myself?

Day 103
What do I most admire in others?

Day 104
What excuses do I use that hold me back?

Day 105
If I was to give myself advice, what would it be?

Day 106
I am showing integrity when...

Day 107
How do I "give forward"?

Day 108
I am worth…

Day 109
How do I create?

Day 110
What are my personal values?

Day 111
What does love mean to me?

Day 112
Who do I need to forgive and why?

Day 113
What blocks me from forgiving?

Day 114
What deflates my drive and love of life?

Day 115
What is my biggest regret, and how would I change it?

Day 116
If there was no risk of failure, what would I do?

Day 117
What have I learned from my past?

Day 118
How can I change my image to reflect the person I want to be?

Day 119
What positive strategy can I use for overcoming obstacles?

Day 120
What's my happy ending?

REFLECTION

In this wrap-up section, you will be asked to reflect on your experience. Note your answers below.

Reflection Question 1
What did I discover about myself?

Reflection Question 2
Are there any changes that I see myself making based off of what I have learned?

Reflection Question 3
How will I use this experience to help "give forward" to other people?

REFLECTION

In this wrap-up section, you will be asked to reflect on your experience. Note your answers below.

Reflection Question 4
How do I talk to myself differently?

Reflection Question 5
Who am I now?

"Stuck" Poem

I was not in a good place when I wrote this. I remember feeling like I was in this deep, deep pit and there was no way out. The sides were wet and muddy, and whenever I would try to climb out, I would slide all the way down again. When I looked up to see the opening of the pit... all I saw was a pinprick of light. It was so far away. I felt hopeless and so very alone.

This was an automatic writing piece where I just closed my eyes and freed my mind. Then I just wrote what came through and didn't even acknowledge or consider what I wrote until the end. When I did finally read it, it was very telling of where my head and heart were at.

Stuck

I feel stuck between dreams and reality...
    between light and darkness...
    between land and sea...

Crying doesn't help like so many say.

It just reminds me I'm sad
    and reminds me how much I hate to cry.

I remember when I used to laugh, to smile.
    I loved laughing, making others laugh with me...
    such a challenge, such fun
    to get others to stop and share a laugh and a smile.

I feel so lost and yet not looking for "home"
    even though "home" is my foundation.

My "home" wasn't what I thought...
    too many secrets, too many barriers,
    too many excuses and denials...
    good times, laughter, glances, but...sadness.

No...I don't want that "home."

So, what do I want?
    what will bring back the light,
    the scent of a flower,
    the warmth when I look in the mirror?

I need to take care of myself...so what does that mean?

Do I not think of him, or is it about him?

I'm bitter because he wants her and not me.

He says it is not that simple, but it's her arms he sleeps in.

It hurts; it makes me want to cry, and I don't want to cry.

It makes me angry because I know I am a good person,
    and yet he doesn't want me.

Dreams seem safer than reality,
    light hurts and darkness hides things

Crawling up onto land seems too hard.
    It is easier to just sink in the sea.

But I can't...It is just not me.

So I go back to being stuck
    and hoping one day I will break free.

About the Author

Life is a bunch of opportunities and chances to look in new directions.

I am about helping others, staying true to myself, and being a part of something bigger than me. I believe life is what you make of it and I don't intend to be a visitor in it. In regards to my adult life, it started with getting my bachelors degree in

psychology. After finishing college, I worked in a non-profit organization for children who were struggling with emotional, sexual, and/ or physical abuse. I did that for a number of years but found myself starting to fall into a dark place. It took its toll on me seeing so many children struggling and in so much pain. I needed to step away to reground myself, but I always knew I would find my way back to them one day. So, I switched gears and decided to focus on my creative side. I ended up being absorbed into the marketing world of Silicon Valley's high tech industry. I did that for over a decade, but after my husband passed, I took some time to get my feet back under me. When

I was ready, I went back to college to get my elementary school teaching credential and have been blessed to work with hundreds of students and their families over the years. Through healing and teaching, I rediscovered my passion for writing and became an author. My life journey has been filled with positive and challenging experiences, such as being a single mom, a widow, a rape survivor, a teacher, a life coach, and an author. This has allowed me to acquire unique experiences that have helped me connect with people. We all have gifts to share with the world...ones that help heal it and us. What gifts do you share?

The Adventures of Hank and Calle

From the author of "Calle's Story"

A book with two parts...

...A children's travel series that involves Hank the Bear

and a journey of healing for a dad and his daughter.

The Adventures of Hank and Calle is a sweet story of healing, but it is also a

children's travel-book series that allows readers' families to partake in the same routes that Hank and Calle travel. Each book shares another adventure traveled by this trio. It has a map of their route and shares the locations that they visit. And with each trip, they gain a little more happiness in their hearts and begin their much needed healing.

Here is their story...

After the recent death of her mom, Calle and her bear Hank show courage and curiosity as they travel the world with her dad on his engineering projects. Her mom's last request was that Calle take Hank with her on all of her adventures. Along the way, they share their healing by finding fun, adventure, and new things to appreciate.

Join this dynamic trio on these special journeys. Be ready to be immersed and inspired by their strength, their struggles, and their unwavering love for each other. There is something for everyone in this series...children and adults alike.

Calle's Story

From the author of "The Adventures of Hank and Calle"

Have you ever felt lost and confused...

...not sure how to explain how you feel?

Calle and her dad tackle these feelings together and come out building something stronger.

Calle's Story is a compelling and yet witty story of a young girl who triumphantly walks the road to healing after losing her mom to cancer. She, along with her dad and trusted friend, Hank the Bear, embark on this powerful life's journey of self discovery and healing.

It is a story full of strong lessons, compassion, and empowering ideas. It enlightens readers of "how to find the gifts in the yuck."

Along the way, readers will be able to celebrate Calle's moments of triumph where she starts to see glimpses of the laughter and happiness that used to fill her life.

Readers of all ages have something to gain from reading Calle's Story. She has a lot to share.

Remeber to find
the gifts in the
yuck.

Look for
something
extraordinary
today.

Look up and smile at someone today. What did they do?

Made in the USA
Coppell, TX
14 December 2021

68192932R00044